Saxophone Exam Pack

ABRSM Grade 2

Selected from the 2018–2021 syllabus

Name

Date

C000143495

Contents

Consultant Editor for ABRSM: David Blackwell
Footnotes: Anthony Burton

Other pieces for Grade 2

Alternative pieces for E♭ and B♭ saxophones are listed in the piano accompaniment booklet.

First published in 2017 by ABRSM (Publishing) Ltd,
a wholly owned subsidiary of ABRSM, 4 London Wall Place,
London EC2Y 5AU, United Kingdom
© 2017 by The Associated Board of the Royal Schools of Music
Distributed worldwide by Oxford University Press

Unauthorized photocopying is illegal
All rights reserved. No part of this publication
may be reproduced, recorded or transmitted
in any form or by any means without the
prior permission of the copyright owner.

Music origination by Julia Bovee and Katie Johnston (Sight-reading)
Cover by Kate Benjamin & Andy Potts
Printed in England by Halstan & Co. Ltd, Amersham, Bucks.,
on materials from sustainable sources.

It is **illegal** to make unauthorized copies of this copyright music.

Allegretto

No. 6 from *Kurze und leichte Klavierstücke*, H 198

Arranged by David Blackwell

C. P. E. Bach
(1714–88)

Carl Philipp Emanuel Bach was the second surviving son of Johann Sebastian Bach, and in his time – the early Classical period – the most important composer in northern Germany. He pioneered a new 'expressive style' which influenced the next generation of composers; Beethoven said that some of his keyboard works 'should be in the possession of every true artist'. This Allegretto, with its gentle, pastoral feeling, comes from a collection of 'Short and Easy Piano Pieces' which was published in Berlin in 1766.

© 2017 by The Associated Board of the Royal Schools of Music

It is **illegal** to make unauthorized copies of this copyright music.

Polka

Arranged by Nancy Litten

M. I. Glinka
(1804–57)

The polka is a lively ballroom dance of Czech origin which became an international craze in the 1840s. This example, originally a solo piano piece, was written by the Russian composer Mikhail Ivanovich Glinka on 12 April 1849 at the home of Vasily Pavlovich Engelhardt, an astronomer friend of Glinka who assembled a collection of his manuscripts. The arrangement adds a four-bar introduction, then gives Glinka's melody to the saxophone over the customary 'oom-pah' accompaniment of the polka.

© 2017 by The Associated Board of the Royal Schools of Music

It is **illegal** to make unauthorized copies of this copyright music.

A:3

The Ploughboy

Arranged by Hywel Davies

22/2/18

William Shield
(1748–1829)

Although it is included in a well-known album of folk songs, 'The Ploughboy' is actually from a 1787 opera, *The Farmer*, by the English theatre composer William Shield. In this jaunty song, the singer describes his lowly origins as 'a flaxen-headed cowboy, as simple as may be', and next 'a merry ploughboy, who whistled o'er the lea' (field). He goes on to predict his social climb from footman to butler, then steward, Member of Parliament and finally peer (member of the House of Lords), concluding 'You'll forget the little ploughboy...'.

© Copyright 2014 by Boosey & Hawkes Music Publishers Ltd
Reproduced by permission of Boosey & Hawkes Music Publishers Ltd.

It is **illegal** to make unauthorized copies of this copyright music.

Farewell for a Fox

B:1

Aubrey Beswick
(1933–2013)

Aubrey Beswick taught the clarinet and saxophone and conducted bands in the Leeds area in northern England. His compositions include music for concert band, a popular album of songs called *Pick 'n' Choose*, and *Six for Sax*, a collection of pieces featuring animals. The first of these, 'Farewell for a Fox', is song-like in character, with long, expressive phrases.

© Copyright 1986 by Universal Edition (London) Ltd., London
All rights reserved. Reproduced with kind permission from *Six for Sax for Alto Saxophone* (UE 17973) and *Repertoire Explorer Tenor Saxophone* (UE 21612).

It is **illegal** to make unauthorized copies of this copyright music.

B:2

Waltz

No. 13 from *24 Easy Pieces*, Op. 39

Arranged by Alan Bullard

D. B. Kabalevsky
(1904–87)

Dmitry Borisovich Kabalevsky was one of the leading Russian composers of the 20th century. He had a special interest in music for children: he developed a system of musical education, and wrote songs, concertos for young soloists and a set of *24 Easy Pieces*. This one is in the dance rhythm of the waltz, with smooth four-bar phrases.

© Copyright 1967 by Anglo Soviet Music Press Ltd
This arrangement © Copyright 2017 by Anglo Soviet Music Press Ltd. Reproduced by permission of Boosey & Hawkes Music Publishers Ltd.

It is **illegal** to make unauthorized copies of this copyright music.

DEF#AB D   # listen to demo

Greenmarket Square

B:3

No. 2 from *Globetrotters*

22/2/18

DO THE TONGUING

Ros Stephen
(born 1972)

Joyful township swing ♩ = *c*.112 (♪♪ = ♪³♪)

Ros Stephen is a violinist, composer and arranger who is a specialist in the tango, and has played and written for several pop and jazz projects. This piece from her popular *Globetrotters* series is named after a long-established street market in Cape Town, South Africa. It is written as a song in the style of township jazz, with lyrics that describe the pleasure of shopping on a sunny day for juicy fruit, spices and the ingredients for a tasty stew. The swing rhythm and articulation of the music communicate the carefree character of the words.

© Oxford University Press 2012 and 2013
Reproduced by permission. All rights reserved.

It is **illegal** to make unauthorized copies of this copyright music.

Prelude

from *L'Arlésienne*, Suite No. 1

Arranged by ABRSM

Georges Bizet
(1838–75)

In 1872, the French composer Georges Bizet wrote incidental music for Alphonse Daudet's *L'Arlésienne* (The Girl from Arles), a play set in the south of France; he also arranged some of the music as an orchestral suite. The scoring in both versions includes a saxophone, one of the first significant uses of the recently invented instrument in an orchestral work. The opening Prelude, as well as the Suite, begins with a unison melody based on an old Provençal tune called 'March of the Three Kings'.

© 2017 by The Associated Board of the Royal Schools of Music

 It is **illegal** to make unauthorized copies of this copyright music.

Boston Blues

Pete Churchill
(born 1961)

Pete Churchill is an experienced jazz singer, pianist and conductor as well as a songwriter, composer and arranger. He taught at the Guildhall School of Music & Drama in London for almost 20 years, and is now Professor of Jazz Composition at the Royal Academy of Music and Director of the London Vocal Project. This newly written piece gains its blues character from its use of the flattened fifth of the 'blues scale' (A♭ in the key of D minor) and its offbeat accents.

© 2017 by The Associated Board of the Royal Schools of Music

C:3

New Document

No. 4 from *Jazz@Etudes* for Saxophone

Mark Nightingale
(born 1967)

It is **illegal** to make unauthorized copies of this copyright music.

Mark Nightingale is a jazz trombonist in many groups including his own quintet and big band. He began writing for jazz bands while he was a member of the National Youth Jazz Orchestra, and is now much in demand as a composer and arranger. He has also written a large amount of music for young performers. *Jazz@Etudes* is a collection of studies with computer-themed titles.

© Copyright 2004 Warwick Music Ltd
All rights reserved. Reproduced by kind permission from Mark Nightingale: *Jazz@Etudes* for Saxophone.

Scales and arpeggios

SCALES

from memory
tongued *and* slurred

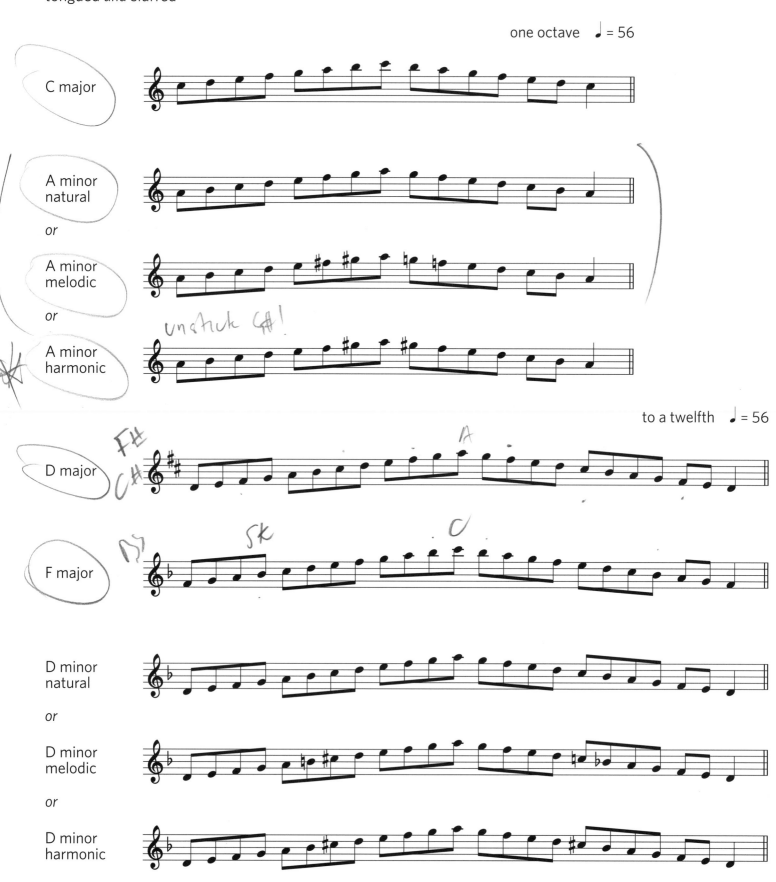

ARPEGGIOS

from memory
tongued *and* slurred

one octave ♪ = 84

C major

A minor

to a twelfth ♪ = 84

D major

F major

D minor

Sight-reading

Sight-reading

Sight-reading

Sight-reading